Fun for ALL!™

Picture Hunt

Visit us at www.kidsbooks.com/answers for the answers.

SEARCH & FIND® WITH GAMES

- Clown
- Dog
- Dominos (3)
- Flies (3)
- Giraffe
- Igloo
- Jacks (8)
- Joker
- King
- Knight
- Ladybug
- Mermaid
- Pawn
- Pig
- Queen
- Rabbits (2)
- Red dice (3)
- Tic-tac-toe
- Thimble
- Yo-yo

SEARCH & FIND®
WITH RAINBOWS

- Asparagus
- Bee
- Butterflies (4)
- Cat
- Drums (2)
- Funnel
- Guitars (2)
- Hard hats (4)
- Icicle
- Ladybug
- Lock
- Nutcrackers (2)
- Ping-pong ball
- Scissors
- Telephones (5)
- Watch

SEARCH & FIND®
IN OUTER SPACE

- Astronauts (5)
- Barrel
- Blue lightbulb
- Bolt
- Bottle
- CD
- Cow

- Flying horse
- Golf ball
- House
- Kazoo
- Magnet
- Monkey
- Parking meter

- Rubber d
- Ship
- Starfish
- Teacup
- Telescope

SEARCH & FIND®
WITH GAMES

- Clown
- Dog
- Dominos (3)
- Flies (3)
- Giraffe
- Igloo

- Jacks (8)
- Joker
- King
- Knight
- Ladybug
- Mermaid
- Pawn

- Pig
- Queen
- Rabbits (2)
- Red dice (3)
- Tic-tac-toe
- Thimble
- Yo-yo

SPECTACULAR CIRCUS SIDESHOW ATTRACTIONS & OTHERS

SWORD SWALLOWER

SMALLEST PERSON

STRONG MAN

BEARDED LADY

RUBBER MAN

SIAMESE TWINS

EXIT

SPOT WHAT

POPCORN

KINDLY CONTROL YOURSELF

ATTEN

Up!,
r to see,
s in town,
t guaranteed!

s the high-flying
ellini Brothers,
rform death-defying,
upefying stunts above us,

With jugglers juggling,
Clowns clowning around,
The high wire dare-devils,
Dare-devilling astound,

A better time cannot
Be found anywhere,
So come on down,
To the Circus & Fair

CREAM
ICE CREAM
ICE CANDY
CAK

fountain of youth

SPECTACULAR GORGE

THE LILLIPUT AMATEUR THEATRICAL SOCIETY
presents
MAGICAL MAX AND HIS SUITCASE OF SORCERY

- Apple core
- Avocado
- Balloons (3)
- Bees (4)
- Blue candles (6)
- Bunch of grapes
- Carrot
- Chili peppers (2)
- Corn on the cob
- Cupcake
- Gingerbread man
- Halved tomato
- Hot dogs (2)
- Mermaid
- Muffin
- Paprika

SEARCH & FIND®
IN A BOTTLE

- Astronaut
- Boat
- Dog
- Doughnut
- Emus (2)
- Four-leaf clover
- Globe
- Guitar
- Lemons (3)

- Owl
- Parrot
- Peacock
- Pineapple
- Pots of gold (7)
- Santa Claus
- Sleigh
- Tiger
- Watch

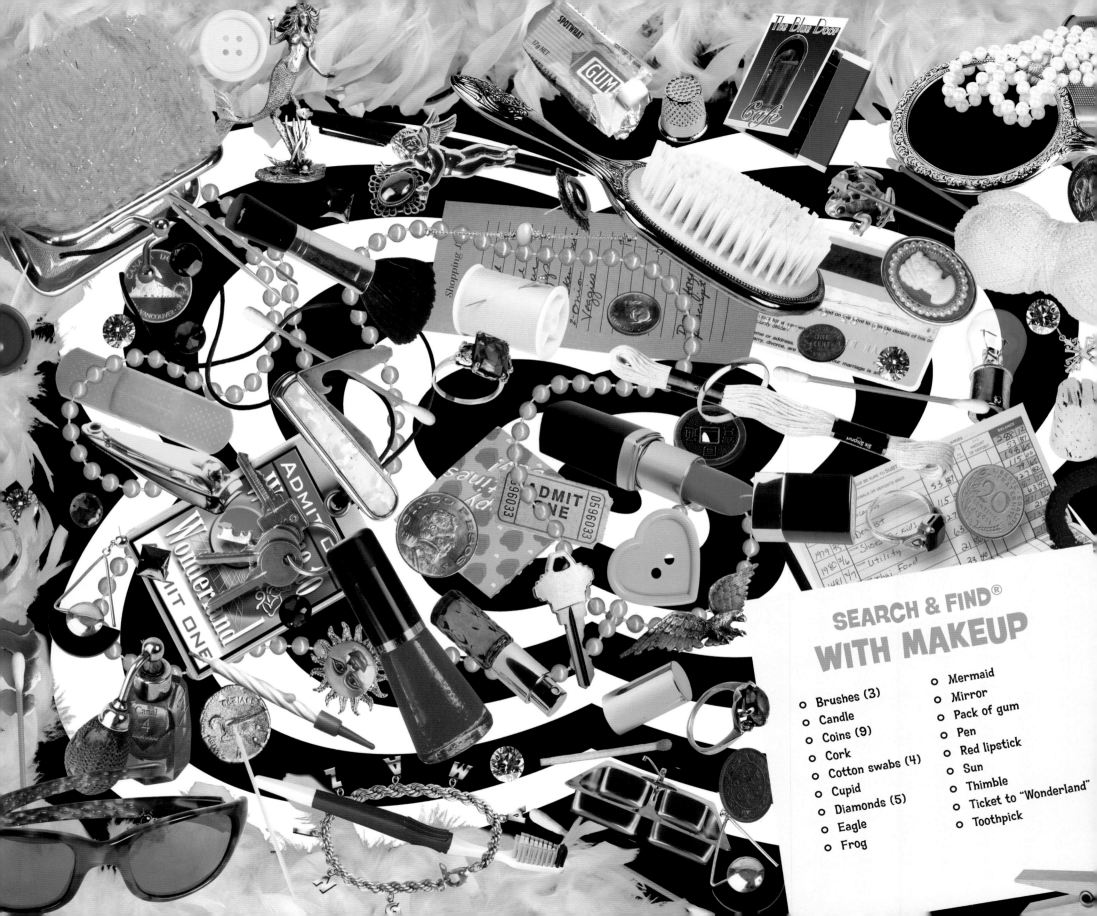

SEARCH & FIND®
WITH MAKEUP

- Brushes (3)
- Candle
- Coins (9)
- Cork
- Cotton swabs (4)
- Cupid
- Diamonds (5)
- Eagle
- Frog
- Mermaid
- Mirror
- Pack of gum
- Pen
- Red lipstick
- Sun
- Thimble
- Ticket to "Wonderland"
- Toothpick

- Ball of yarn
- Ballet shoes (2)
- Banjo
- Bow tie
- Bowling ball
- Compass
- Egg
- Elephant
- Fan
- Frying pan
- Garden gnome
- Guitar
- Knife
- Pie
- Stapler
- Swan
- Tuning fork
- Wagon wheel

SEARCH & FIND®
UNDER THE SEA

- Anchor
- Catfish
- Coin
- Crab
- Door
- Ducks (4)
- Jellyfish
- Oars (2)
- Octopus
- Pearl
- Scuba divers (4)
- Seagulls (2)
- Seahorse
- Seal
- Skulls (2)
- Submarine

Amazing **Places**

WEATHER

THE FISHMONGERS

test signal - please standby -

Next Millennium's Forecast

Strong solar winds

Expected high +5000 degrees

Nighttime low 0

WEATHER

NEWS

WORLD PEACE

NEXT

ever be ICK GAIN

Doctors recommend

Today's special*

*So is tomorrow and yesterday

et lots of exercise

Spot *Noodle*

NEW *EARWAX FLAVOR*

SNEW

Next Millennium's Forecast

WEATHER

FM 004.00 stereo

SPOT WHAT

SEARCH & FIND® WITH TELEVISIONS

- Apple
- Baboon
- Bear
- Cameras (2)
- Dolphins (4)
- Donkey
- Flowerpot
- Jack
- Lightbulb

- Mermaid
- Microphone
- Poodle
- Skier
- Skunk
- Spider
- Tomahawk
- Trombone
- Wolf

SEARCH & FIND® IN A PUZZLE

- Blackboard
- Calculator
- Car
- Cheetah
- Cowboy
- Egg
- Footprint
- Stack of gold bars
- Guitar
- Kite
- Matchstick
- Mug
- Scissors
- Seashell
- Truck

SEARCH & FIND®
WITH TRICKS

- Bicycle
- Binoculars
- Bubbles (2)
- Cherry
- Chickens (2)
- Cymbals (2)
- Domino
- Flipper
- Hair bow

- Joker
- Key
- Lock
- Piggy bank
- Popcorn
- Roller coaster
- Sunglasses
- Toaster
- Trophy